The

UNITED

STATES of

QUiRK

150 Trivia Questions About All Things American

TOULA & JAMES MESSER

Contents

Disclaimer

Although the publisher and the author have made every effort to ensure that the information in this book was correct at the time of press and while this publication is designed to provide accurate information in regard to the subject matter covered, the publisher and the author assume no responsibility for errors, inaccuracies, omissions, or any other inconsistencies herein and hereby disclaim any liability to any party for any loss, damage, or disruption caused by errors or omissions, whether such errors or omissions result from negligence, accident, or any other cause.

Introduction:

America is a land of wonder, diversity, and quirkiness. From its natural beauty to its unique traditions, there is always something new to discover.

The United States of Quirk, celebrates the quirkiness of America. With 150 trivia questions, you'll learn about the hidden gems of America, from its unique traditions to its unusual laws. You'll also learn about the people who make America great, from its famous inventors to its everyday heroes.

The United States of Quirk is the perfect book for anyone who loves America. It's a fun and informative way to learn about the country's rich history and culture. So sit back, relax, and enjoy the ride. The United States of Quirk is a journey you won't soon forget.

Here are just a few of the things that make America such a special place:

Natural beauty: America is home to some of the most stunning natural scenery in the world, from the snow-capped peaks of the Rocky Mountains to the sun-kissed beaches of California. The Grand Canyon, Yellowstone National Park, and Yosemite National Park are just a few of the many natural wonders that America has to offer.

Rich history: America is a young country, but it has a rich and complex history that is full of fascinating stories. From the American Revolution, to the Civil War, to the Civil Rights Movement, America's history is one of constant change and progress. The Statue of Liberty, the Lincoln Memorial, and the White House are just a few of the many historical landmarks that America has to offer.

Diverse culture: America is a melting pot of cultures from all over the world, and this diversity is one of its greatest strengths. From the food, to the music, to the art, America's culture is vibrant and exciting.

The United States has a rich culinary history that reflects the diverse cultures of its people. Some of the most popular American dishes include pizza, burgers, and tacos. American music is also incredibly diverse, with genres ranging from country, to hip hop, to jazz. And

American art is just as varied, with artists like Andy Warhol and Jackson Pollock creating some of the most iconic works of the 20th century.

Opportunity: America is a land of opportunity, where anyone can achieve their dreams if they are willing to work hard. This is the American Dream, and it is one of the things that makes America such a special place.

The American Dream is the belief that anyone, regardless of where they were born or what class they were born into, can attain their own version of success in a society in which upward mobility is possible for everyone.

Oprah Winfrey was born into poverty in Mississippi, but she became one of the most successful talk show hosts and media moguls in the world, and Steve Jobs was adopted as a baby and raised by a middle-class family in California. He dropped out of college but eventually founded Apple, one of the most successful technology companies in the world.

Then there's the quirkiness. America is a country where people are free to be themselves, and that often leads to some pretty interesting and unusual things. Here are just a few examples:

- In Oregon, it's illegal to throw a snowball at a car.

- In Idaho, it is illegal to ride a merry-go-round on a Sunday.

- In Ohio, it's illegal to get a fish drunk within state lines.

- In North Carolina, it is illegal to sing off-key.

These are just a few of the many quirks that make America such a unique and special place. So next time you're feeling down, just remember that there's a place where it's illegal to get a fish drunk within state lines. It's enough to make you smile.

I really hope you enjoy The United States of Quirk: 150 Q&A About All Things American!

QUESTION

?

Who added the phrase "So help me God" to the end of the Presidential Oath of Office during his inauguration in 1789?

A George Washington

B John Adams

C Thomas Jefferson

ANSWER

A   *George Washington*

The Presidential Oath of Office has been delivered in that way ever since, which is interesting because of the separation of church and state. George Washington was an Anglican. It took a further 172 years for the first and only Catholic President, John F. Kennedy, to come to office until Joe Biden was sworn in in 2021.

QUESTION

?

Who especially loves a Bratwurst sausage?

A The people of Wisconsin

B The people of New York

C The people of Oklahoma

A   *The people of Wisconsin*

It is believed that the millions of German immigrants who moved to America during the mid-19th and early 20th centuries introduced a love of Bratwurst and primarily in Wisconsin. This is especially true in Wisconsin where more than 40 percent of residents today have German ancestry. New Yorkers invented the all-beef frank 'Hot Dog,' topped with sauerkraut and spicy brown mustard, with optional onions, and the specialty of Oklahoma is a sausage smoked over hickory.

QUESTION

?

In which state is the town that comes alphabetically last in the whole of America?

A California

B Nevada

C New Hampshire

ANSWER

A   *California*

California is home to Zzyzx (pronounced Z-eye-zix), which was previously known as Camp Soda Springs; a big difference as you can see. A gentleman by the name of Curtis Howe Springer changed the name to Zzyzx. He also created the Zzyzx Mineral Spring and Health Spa, brought in a zoo, and sold visitors the water that he had bottled from the spring.

QUESTION

?

The original version of (Get Your Kicks on) Route 66 was a massive hit in 1946 for which singer?

A Sammy Davis Jr

B Bing Crosby

C Nat King Cole

ANSWER

C   *Nat King Cole*

The song was a hit for Nat King Cole as part of the King Cole Trio. Route 66, the actual road, was said by the U.S. Route 66 Highway Association to be "the shortest, best, and most scenic route from Chicago through St. Louis to Los Angeles." Many locations from the route were mentioned in the song, including, 'Flagstaff, Arizona. Don't forget Winona,' which inspired country singer Wynonna Judd, born as Christina Ciminella, to make it her stage name.

QUESTION

?

The first game of what was played in Springfield, Massachusetts in 1891?

A Basketball

B Baseball

C Football

ANSWER

A *Basketball*

Springfield is the birthplace of basketball, as it was invented in 1891 by Springfield college instructor and graduate student James Naismith. Springfield is a common place name with 20 towns across the states. It's so common that even the Simpsons live there!

QUESTION

?

The town of Choccolocco is in which state?

A Texas

B Mississippi

C Alabama

ANSWER

C *Alabama*

Choccolocco apparently once had a
'monster.' It turned out to be local resident
called Neal Williamson, who as a teenager
in the sixties, would wear a sheet and cow
skull, and then jump out from behind trees
to startle passing motorists.

QUESTION

?

The world's tallest thermometer is located in which town in the U.S.?

A Williams, Arizona

B El Paso, Texas

C Baker, California

C *Baker, California*

Built in 1992 next to the Bun Boy restaurant, The Worlds Tallest Thermometer is a landmark in the town of Baker, California, U.S. The 134ft (41m) high steel structure originally cost $700,000 and was built to commemorate the weather record temperature of 134 °F recorded in nearby Death Valley on July 10, 1913. The electric sign, which weighs an enormous 76,812lbs, can be seen clearly from Interstate 15 and is held together by 125 cubic yards of concrete, which stops it from snapping in strong winds.

QUESTION

?

How many feet (approximately) is the South Rim of the Grand Canyon above sea level?

A 700ft

B 7,000ft

C 70,000ft

B   *7,000ft*

The Grand Canyon is 277 miles long, 18 miles wide (at its widest point), and 1.2 million acres (1,902 square miles), which makes it the 11th largest national park in the United States.

QUESTION

?

The United States has the largest road network in the world, with more than how many miles of road?

A 2 million

B 3 million

C 4 million

ANSWER

C *4 million*

The heaviest traveled interstate is California's I-405, which carries around 400,000 vehicles per day. The least traveled road is the U.S. Route 160, which runs through the now deserted Navajo Nation.

24

QUESTION

?

According to a survey this percentage of American car owners cannot remember the last time they washed their cars.

A 2%

B 7%

C 10%

B   *10%*

10 percent of car owners can't remember when they last washed their cars, and according to a survey of 2,000 Americans, 35 percent of car owners have no idea how often they should wash their cars. Perhaps when they discover that, according to a university-based bacterial study, car interiors can often be dirtier than toilets with 146 types of bacteria found on the steering wheels of the vehicles tested, this percentage might get lower!

QUESTION

? A small town in the Fairbanks North Star Borough of Alaska is famous for which one of the following activities?

A Stargazing and seeing the Northern Lights

B Celebrating Christmas every day

C World-record husky racing

ANSWER

B **Celebrating Christmas every day**

In North Pole, Alaska it is Christmas every day. From the local street names of Kris Kringle Drive and Mistletoe Lane, to its year-round Christmas decorations and Santa Claus House; a cute Christmas store with walls covered in letters from children to Santa and the giant Santa statue right outside.

QUESTION

?

Truth or Consequences in New Mexico was previously called what?

A Questa

B Palomas Hot Springs

C Santa Rosa

ANSWER

B *Palomas Hot Springs*

Palomas Hot Springs changed to Truth or Consequences on April 1, 1950. The name was that of an NBC radio show contest (and also the names of a successful TV show). To honor the radio show's 10th year, the presenter Ralph Edwards offered to host the show from any town that was willing to change its name to Truth or Consequences. A special election was called and the townsfolk voted in favor of the name change. For many years after, Ralph Edwards visited Truth or Consequences to celebrate the fiesta that was named after him.

QUESTION

?

How many versions of the U.S. flag have there been?

A 13

B 27

C 50

B 27

Since the founding of the United States in 1776, there have been 27 different versions of the flag featuring the stars and stripes. Currently, there are 50 stars on the flag of the United States: one for each of the 50 states and 13 stripes: one for each of the original colonies.

QUESTION

?

Buttzville, Bargaintown, and Loveladies are all towns in which state?

A New Hampshire

B New York

C New Jersey

ANSWER

C *New Jersey*

Buttzville was founded in 1839 by Michael Robert Buttz who named it for his son, Liam Oakes Buttz. When a property developer had to sell property lots more cheaply than he had hoped, it became Bargaintown. Loveladies took its name from a local hunter and sportsman, Thomas Lovelady. If, in 1893, U.S. House Representative Lucas Miller from Wisconsin had had his way with a proposed constitutional amendment, the entire country would have been called the 'United States of Earth.'

QUESTION

? How far into the distance can you see from Bryce Canyon on a clear day?

A 2 miles

B 10 miles

C 100 miles

ANSWER

C *100 miles*

Bryce Canyon National Park in Utah was
settled by Mormon pioneers in the 1850s.
It is named after Ebenezer Bryce, who
homesteaded in the area in 1874. Due to
the high elevation, exceptional air quality
and low humidity, it is said that you can
see at least 100 miles into the distance
from many of the park's viewpoints.

QUESTION

?

The first Thanksgiving Day was celebrated in Plymouth, Massachusetts in which year…and did they eat turkey?

A 1615

B 1621

C 1629

ANSWER

B   *1621*

The 'first Thanksgiving' was a three-day feast celebrated by the Pilgrims after their first harvest in the New World in October 1621. It was also attended by 90 Native American Wampanoag people and 53 survivors of the Mayflower. No turkey was consumed. They ate a feast of freshly killed deer, assorted wildfowl and fish, and a native variety of corn called flint. An earlier Thanksgiving celebration in Virginia in 1619 was held by English settlers, who had recently landed at Berkeley Hundred, Virginia, aboard the ship 'Margaret.'

QUESTION

?

The longest road in America, which stretches for more than 3,365 miles from Boston, Massachusetts, to Portland, Oregon, is which U.S. Route?

A U.S. Route 10

B U.S. Route 20

C U.S. Route 93

ANSWER

B | ***U.S. Route 20***

U.S. Route 20 or U.S. Highway 20 (US 20) is an east-west United States Numbered Highway that runs from the Pacific Northwest all the way east across the United States to New England. Interstate 10 is the southernmost cross-country highway and is the fourth-longest Interstate in the United States at 2,460 miles (3,960km), and also goes from east to west, stretching from the I-95 in Jacksonville, Florida, to the Pacific Ocean in Santa Monica, California.

?

Mobster Bugsy Siegel oversaw the building of The Flamingo Hotel & Casino, which opened in December of 1946. In which year did it make a profit?

A 1948

B 1958

C 1968

A   *1948*

Bugsy Siegel, an American mobster with the Luciano crime family, went over his $1 million budget with construction costs reaching $6 million to build the luxury 105-room Flamingo Hotel & Casino, on what became the Las Vegas Strip. The opening week saw losses of $300,000. Finally, in 1948, the hotel made a $4 million profit. Sadly, Siegel was no longer alive to see this, as he had been shot dead by a sniper on June 20, 1947, through a window of his girlfriend's Linden Drive mansion in Beverly Hills, California.

QUESTION

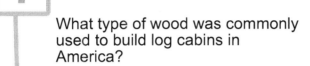

?

What type of wood was commonly used to build log cabins in America?

A Pine

B Oak

C Maple

43

ANSWER

A   *Pine*

Pine is a great option to use when building a log cabin. It is an abundant species, grows straight, and is often very affordable. Eastern White Pine is the most versatile as it is extremely strong, is weather resistant, and looks attractive.

QUESTION

?

When did Washington D.C. become the capital of the United States?

A 1788

B 1789

C 1790

C   *1790*

On July 16, 1790, after seven years of negotiation by members of the U.S. Congress, it was declared that the city of Washington in the District of Columbia was to be the permanent capital of the United States, where among many other notable locations the White House, Capitol Building and Washington Monument can all be found. New York City was the first capital of the United States. George Washington took the oath of office to become the first U.S. President, from the balcony of the old City Hall.

?

In which state is The Alamo to be found?

A Arizona

B Nevada

C Texas

ANSWER

C   *Texas*

The Alamo is located in San Antonio, and was designated as a UNESCO World Heritage site in 2015. It was named after the abundant cottonwood trees, which are type of poplar, as 'alamo' is the Spanish word for cottonwood. The trees are the fastest growing tree in North America, adding up to 6ft (2m) of height per year, with the female trees being the ones that produce the fluffy white substance that gives the trees their name. 'King of the Wild Frontier' David 'Davy' Crockett fought and died at the Battle of the Alamo, on the morning of March 6, 1836 at the age of 49.

?

The Greenbrier Hotel in White Sulphur Springs, West Virginia, is known for its:

A Ghostly apparitions

B Underground bunker

C Luxurious spa treatments

B   *Underground bunker*

The massive underground bunker was meant to serve as an emergency shelter for the United States Congress during the Cold War and was code named 'Project Greek Island.' The bunker contained a dormitory, kitchen and hospital. It also had a broadcast center for members of Congress (with changeable seasonal backdrops to allow it to appear as if broadcasts were being made from Washington, D.C.).

QUESTION

?

Cawker City, Kansas, is home to the biggest ball of what?

A Wool

B Rubber bands

C Twine

ANSWER

C *Twine*

Frank Stoeber created a ball with 1.6 million ft (490,000m) of twine and an 11ft diameter (3.4m). An open-air gazebo was built over the ball to protect it and every August a 'Twine-a-thon' is held and more twine is added to the ball so it continues to grow ever larger.

QUESTION

?

Eek is a small town in which state?

A Dakota

B Alaska

C Idaho

B *Alaska*

Eek, Alaska, is around 400 miles from Anchorage. It has less than 500 residents and its name was derived from the Eskimo word for 'two eyes.'

QUESTION

?

What is the most populous city in the United States?

A Los Angeles

B New York City

C Chicago

ANSWER

B *New York City*

New York City has almost 9 million residents, followed by Los Angeles and Chicago which have more than 2.5 million residents in each.

?

Where is the world's most impressive collection of hoodoos to be found in the U.S.?

A Wyoming

B Utah

C Idaho

B *Utah*

Hoodoos are irregular columns of rock that exist on every continent, but Bryce Canyon has the largest concentration found anywhere on Earth. You might have also heard of them being referred to as tent rocks, fairy chimneys, or earth pyramids. They are usually tall, thin spires of softer rock topped by harder, less easily eroded rock that protects the columns from the elements.

QUESTION

?

What is the only state in the United States that grows coffee beans commercially?

A Hawai'i

B California

C Florida

A *Hawai'i*

There are about 790 coffee farms in Hawai'i with the largest growing district in Kona, which is on the Big Island of Hawai'i in the State of Hawai'i. The beans are grown in volcanic soil and are still picked by hand. Royal Kona coffee is served in all McDonald's restaurants throughout Hawai'i.

QUESTION

?

Which Utah-Colorado road trip takes you through a region with the highest concentration of dinosaur fossils in the world?

A The Jurassic Trail

B The Dinosaur Diamond Prehistoric Highway

C The Triassic Trek

ANSWER

B **The Dinosaur Diamond Prehistoric Highway**

This diamond-shaped National Scenic Byway spans more than 200,000 acres across the Utah and Colorado border. In 1909, thousands of dinosaur fossils were first unearthed on the Utah side. It was greatly expanded in 1938, making it one of the most significant prehistoric sites in the world.

?

What was specifically unique about a now destructed home that was located about 300ft offshore from the Cape Romano Islands on the gulf coast of Florida?

A It was built underwater

B It was built as a giant aquarium

C It was built dome-shaped

ANSWER

C   *It was built dome-shaped*

Built by the late Bob Lee, the six unusual-looking domes that made up the Cape Romano Dome House sat on stilts above the water. They were 'built to survive hurricanes' but finally succumbed to Hurricane Ian in 2023. Before making the Florida house, Bob built a full-scale model in Gatlinburg, Tennessee, which, unlike the Florida Dome House that is no more, still stands today.

QUESTION

?

What is the national anthem of the United States?

A 'The Star-Spangled Banner'

B 'God Bless America'

C 'America the Beautiful'

ANSWER

A — *'The Star-Spangled Banner'*

In 1931, the U.S. Congress passed a joint resolution, which President Herbert Hoover signed into law, making 'The Star Spangled Banner' the official national anthem of the United States. The lyrics come from a poem written by Francis Scott Key, who was inspired by the U.S. flag.

QUESTION

?

Which quirky store sign located in Los Angeles features a giant pink donut?

A The Randy's Donuts sign

B The Donut Man sign

C The California Donut sign

ANSWER

A *The Randy's Donuts sign*

The sign, located in Inglewood, California is 32ft 6in (9.91m) in diameter. We know this because the owners, the Weintraubs, climbed up onto it with a tape measure and confirmed the measurements. The enormous donut has infiltrated popular culture, featuring in numerous movies, music videos and TV shows, including Arrested Development and The Big Bang Theory.

QUESTION

?

The International Banana Museum contains more than 20,000 items related to bananas. Where is it located?

A Alabama

B Florida

C California

ANSWER

C *California*

The International Banana Museum is a one-room museum in Mecca, California. The museum set a Guinness World Record in 1999 as the largest museum devoted to a single fruit. The owner is clearly bananas about bananas! If the museum ap-peels to you or gets under your skin, perhaps you can slip in a visit!

QUESTION

?

Bald Knob, Weiner, and Greasy Corner, are all towns in which state?

A Arkansas

B Kansas

C Kentucky

ANSWER

A   *Arkansas*

The city of Weiner, Arkansas was originally known as West Prairie. The name was changed in 1881 after the train depot was named Weiner after the engineer who oversaw the construction of the St. Louis Southwestern Railroad.

QUESTION

?

The 36,000 square foot house in Sarasota, Florida built by circus greats John and Mable Ringling is called what?

A The Promised Land

B Ca' d'Zan

C Casa de Shenandoah

B *Ca' d'Zan*

The Ringlings were so inspired by the Venetian Gothic style of the palazzos along the Venice canals that they named their house Ca' d'Zan, which translates from Venetian to "House of John." The Ringlings weren't the only circus people living in the area, Gibsonton, local to Sarasota has largest concentration of retired circus workers in the country!

QUESTION

?

What would you do at Lou Mitchell's which is at the start of Route 66 in Chicago?

A Fill your gas tank

B Buy a collector's guide to the historic route

C Eat breakfast

ANSWER

C   *Eat breakfast*

Jackson Boulevard was the starting point for the original Route 66, with Lou Mitchell's Diner on the right, located near the intersection of Jackson and Jefferson. When Route 66 was created in 1926, commuters found Lou Mitchell's right there waiting for them as the family diner was started by Uncle Lou's father at that location in 1923.

?

Nantucket and Martha's Vineyard, off the coast of Massachusetts, were formed by what?

A — Volcanoes

B — Glaciers

C — Earthquakes

B *Glaciers*

The islands of Martha's Vineyard and Nantucket, as well as the entire Cape Cod peninsula, were formed by the slow movements of massive sheets of ice during the last great Ice Age that pushed up giant mounds of earth and rock.

?

In which state is the Craters of the Moon National Monument to be found?

A Colorado

B Idaho

C Delaware

ANSWER

B *Idaho*

The Craters of the Moon National Monument is a 'weird and scenic landscape,' made up of a vast wonderland of lava flows with scattered islands of cinder cones and sagebrush.

?

According to a book by writer Tom Vanderbilt, when do most car crashes happen?

A Sunny, dry, clear days to sober drivers

B Wet, dark, stormy days to sober drivers

C Sunny, dry, clear days to drunk drivers

A *Sunny, dry, clear days to sober drivers*

Tom Vanderbilt is an American journalist, blogger, and author of the best-selling book, 'Traffic: Why We Drive the Way We Do.' Apart from letting us know when most car crashes happen, he has also said that, to keep drivers alert, many roads that could be straight have curves built into them.

QUESTION

?

Who was the first U.S. President to have a pet alligator?

A John Quincy Adams

B Martin Van Buren

C James K. Polk

ANSWER

A   *John Quincy Adams*

President John Quincy Adams was given an alligator by the Marquis de Lafayette. It was kept in a tub in the then-unfinished East Wing of the White House.

QUESTION

?

Which is the largest lake in the USA?

A Lake Michigan

B Lake Huron

C Lake Superior

ANSWER

C   *Lake Superior*

Lake Superior, the largest lake in the USA, is so big that it holds 1/10th of the Earth's surface fresh water and has enough water to cover all of North and South America in one foot of liquid. If that wasn't magical enough, the local Lake Superior State University offers a unicorn hunting license, although the word 'hunting' was changed to 'questing' in recent years.

?

In which state is one of the world's most spectacular example of erosion to be found?

A Texas

B Colorado

C Arizona

C   *Arizona*

The Grand Canyon is one of the most spectacular examples of erosion anywhere in the world. It averages 10 miles across, is a mile deep, and is 277 miles long, encompassing 278 miles (447km) of the Colorado River, and is located on the ancestral homelands of 11 Associated Tribes. The temperature varies 25 degrees from the top of the Canyon to the bottom, with the highest temperatures found at the lowest elevations inside the Canyon.

QUESTION

?

Archie Karas is best known for doing what in Las Vegas?

A Losing his successful business on the roll of one die

B Turning $50 into $40 million in just over three years

C Winning a hotel in a poker game

ANSWER

B *Turning $50 into $40 million in just over three years*

Originally from Kefalonia in Greece, Archie Karas is famous for once turning $50 into $40 million. From 1992 to 1995, during an infamous Las Vegas winning streak, that came to be known as 'The Run,' he played poker and pool competitively and won. Unable to find new opponents, he turned to other games and within three weeks lost most of what he had won in the previous three years.

QUESTION

?

The first Dunkin' Donuts was opened in which state?

A New York

B Illinois

C Massachusetts

C *Massachusetts*

Originally named 'Open Kettle,' founder William Rosenberg served donuts for five cents and premium cups of coffee for ten cents. It was then renamed Dunkin' Donuts after a brainstorming session in 1950. They now have more than 11,300 Dunkin' restaurants worldwide – that's more than 8,500 restaurants in 41 states across the United States, and more than 3,200 international restaurants in 36 countries!

QUESTION

?

What strange tourist attraction in the USA was created by Barney Smith and his artworks?

A Toilet Seat Museum

B Pillow Museum

C Lampshade Palace

ANSWER

A   *Toilet Seat Museum*

Barney Smith opened the original museum in 1992 in a large garage in his backyard. He created more than 1,400 art pieces out of toilet seats over the course of many decades. In 2019, when Barney was 98, the collection was moved to The Truck Yard, The Colony in Texas.

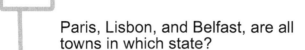

QUESTION

?

Paris, Lisbon, and Belfast, are all towns in which state?

A Maine

B Mississippi

C Michigan

ANSWER

A *Maine*

Maine has 491 cities, towns and plantations, according to the Maine Municipal Association, many of which are named after towns and countries from around the world. These also include Norway, China, Vienna, Frankfurt, Stockholm, and Belgrade.

QUESTION

?

What is the largest state in the United States by area?

A Alaska

B Texas

C California

ANSWER

A *Alaska*

Alaska is the largest state by area (663,267 square miles), comprising more total combined area than the next three largest states of Texas, California and Montana. It originally belonged to Russia but was bought from them on March 30, 1867, for $7.2 million, which was less than 2 cents an acre, for almost 600,000 square miles. Alaska's flag was designed by Benny Benson, a 13-year-old, in 1926, which became the official state flag upon Alaska's adoption into the Union.

QUESTION

?

Which is the only national park that lies in 3 states?

A Dry Tortugas National Park

B Wrangell-St. Elias National Park & Preserve

C Yellowstone National Park

ANSWER

C **Yellowstone National Park**

Even though the official address of Yellowstone National Park is in the state of Wyoming, 96% of Yellowstone is actually in three states - the other two states are Idaho and Montana. Interestingly, the hit TV show 'Yellowstone' filmed most of the first three seasons in Utah, due to the financial incentives offered by the state. Season 5 was filmed exclusively in Montana. The only two other American national parks that lie in multiple states are Death Valley National Park (in California and Nevada), and the Great Smoky Mountains National Park (in Tennessee and North Carolina).

QUESTION

? The Hotel del Coronado was the location for which classic film?

A The Shining

B Psycho

C Some Like It Hot

ANSWER

C   *Some Like It Hot*

Billy Wilder's iconic film Some Like It Hot starred Marilyn Monroe, Tony Curtis and Jack Lemmon. The Hotel Del Coronado, a Victorian masterpiece, is located in San Diego in Southern California, but in the film it played the part of the Seminole Ritz in Florida. Meanwhile, the Timberline Lodge in Oregon, was used as the exterior of the Overlook Hotel, in The Shining.

QUESTION

?

What is the longest river in the United States?

A Mississippi River

B Missouri River

C Colorado River

B *Missouri River*

The Missouri River, a tributary of the Mississippi River, is about 100 miles longer than the Mississippi River, at c. 2,341 miles (3,767km). The shortest river in the world, according to the Guinness Book of World Records, is the Roe River near Great Falls, Montana. It runs from Giant Springs to the Missouri River and is only 201ft (61m) long.

?

Elmer Long created something extremely special with his inheritance. What was it?

A A ranch filled with bottle trees

B Towers made of broken crockery

C A house made of disused car parts

ANSWER

A **A ranch filled with bottle trees**

As a child Elmer Long and his father regularly collected 'treasure' from the desert. Eventually, Elmer inherited that treasure, which was made up of a vast collection of thousands of glass bottles. Not knowing what to do with them at first, he eventually created hundreds of trees and other items covered in bottles, that make up the Bottle Tree Ranch - a magical spectacle of sight and sound. Another Californian architectural marvel are the Watts Towers. Constructed by Sabato Rodia from 1921-1954, they were made from steel, wire mesh, concrete, and objects he found, including broken crockery and so much more.

?

What is the largest state in the United States by population?

A California

B Texas

C Florida

A   *California*

In 2021, with a population of 39.24 million people, California was the most populous state in the United States. Texas came second with a population of 29.53 million people and Florida came third with a population of 21.78 million people. Ken & Barbie are two extra names to have come out of California, having been invented there in 1959 by Ruth Handler. They were named after her children Ken and Barbara, so are in fact brother and sister.

QUESTION

?

The Jules' Undersea Lodge in Florida requires guests to:

A   Scuba dive to reach it

B   Take a boat to reach it

C   Hike to reach it

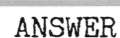
ANSWER

A *Scuba dive to reach it*

The Jules' Undersea Lodge, opened in 1986, is located 30ft (9m) deep at the bottom of the Emerald Lagoon in Key Largo, Florida and is the only underwater hotel in the United States.

QUESTION

? The Kansas part of Route 66 was very short. How many miles long was it?

A 5 miles

B 8 miles

C 13 miles

ANSWER

C *13 miles*

Despite its relatively short section of Route 66, Kansas still has something noteworthy to shout about. Along the route at Galena is the 'Cars on the Route' gas station which houses the original tow truck that inspired the character 'Tow Mater' in the animated Pixar movie 'Cars.'

QUESTION

?

What is the smallest state in the United States by area?

A Rhode Island

B Delaware

C Vermont

ANSWER

C   *Rhode Island*

The last of the original thirteen colonies to become a state, Rhode Island is the smallest state in size, covering an area of 1,214 square miles. It is only 48 miles from North to South and 37 miles from East to West. However, Rhode Island is plenty big enough to be home to the world's largest bug which sits on the roof of the New England Pest Control building in Providence. It's a big blue termite, 58ft (17m) long, 928 times the actual size of a termite size and weighs 4,000lbs.

?

New Orleans' Hotel Monteleone's famous 'Carousel Bar' is a:

A Rooftop bar

B Underwater bar

C Rotating bar

ANSWER

C   *Rotating bar*

The Carousel Bar at the Hotel Monteleone in New Orleans' French Quarter opened for business on September 3, 1949. It has 25 seats which take guests on a Merry-Go-Round ride underneath the colorful carousel top that was added in 1992. Fiber optics have also been installed in the ceiling to create the illusion of stars in the night sky, including a shooting star.

?

No Name, Nowhere, and Nothing, are all towns in which state?

A Maine

B Oregon

C Colorado

C   *Colorado*

No Name is listed as one of 15 of the Weirdest Town Names in America and World's Funniest Town Names and supposedly got its name after the majority of the town's folk wrote "No Name" on a questionnaire about the town's name, under the section, 'Name of Town.' Taking them at their word, "No Name" was officially recorded into the state records as the name of the town. Talking of weird names, Massachusetts's Lake Chargoggagoggmanchauggagoggchaubun agungamaugg has the longest place name in the United States with 46 letters, although locals usually call it Lake Webster, after the closest town.

?

A law was passed in Skamania County, Washington, prohibiting people from doing what?

A Skiing whilst intoxicated

B Slaying a Bigfoot

C Causing catastrophes

ANSWER

B *Slaying a Bigfoot*

In 1969, Skamania County, Washington, passed a law deeming the 'slaying of Bigfoot to be a felony and punishable by 5 years in prison.' Later Bigfoot was designated as an endangered species.

QUESTION

?

Which fast food chain opened its first store in Wichita, Kansas?

A Burger King

B Arby's

C Pizza Hut

ANSWER

C *Pizza Hut*

In 1958, brothers Frank and Dan Carney, students at Wichita University, started a small pizza joint at the corner of Bluff and Kellogg in Wichita. Staffed by friends and family, the business immediately thrived. It is now the largest pizza company in the world with more than 11,000 restaurants in 90 countries.

QUESTION

?

Which of the following is a local food of Hawai'i?

A Spam Musubi

B Sushi

C Pad Thai

A *Spam Musubi*

Spam Musubi is commonly found in Hawai'ian school lunches and local convenience stores. It is often home-made from four simple ingredients: grilled Spam and sushi rice wrapped in nori seaweed and seasoned with Japanese condiment Furikake (mainly made from sesame seeds and seaweed).

QUESTION

?

In the 1940s, Henry Ford made a car from which material?

A Rubber

B Wood

C Soybeans

ANSWER

C **Soybeans**

Henry Ford unveiled the 'Soybean Car' on August 13, 1941. The frame was made of tubular steel, had 14 plastic panels, supposedly made from 'soybean fiber in a phenolic resin with formaldehyde used in the impregnation' attached to it, and was 1000lbs lighter than a steel car.

QUESTION

?

Yellowstone National Park has 700 to 3,000 what per year?

A Visitors

B Earthquakes

C Deaths

B   *Earthquakes*

Yellowstone is one of the most seismically active areas in the United States, resulting from the large network of faults associated with the supervolcano and surrounding tectonic features. The majority of those earthquakes are not felt. One of the associated effects of the tectonic activity is Old Faithful, a cone geyser that has erupted every 44 minutes to two hours and normally lasts from 1.5 to 5 minutes. The eruptions vary in height from 100 to180ft (30m to 55m), averaging 130 to140ft (9 to 12m), according to historical records.

QUESTION

?

Howard Hughes once requested 350 gallons of which flavored ice-cream whilst staying at the Desert Inn, Las Vegas?

A Vanilla Bean

B Tutti Frutti

C Banana Nut

ANSWER

C   *Banana Nut*

After hearing that his favorite flavor of ice cream had been discontinued by Baskin-Robbins, Howard Hughes had his staff put in a special order for the smallest amount that the company could provide, which was a whopping 350 gallons (1,300 liters). It was delivered to the Desert Inn Hotel, which Hughes bought in 1967, after renting the top two floors a year earlier.

QUESTION

? Which is the longest bridge in the United States (and possibly the world)?

A Atchafalaya Basin Bridge

B Lake Pontchartrain Causeway

C Manchac Swamp Bridge

ANSWER

B **Lake Pontchartrain Causeway**

The Lake Pontchartrain Causeway is the longest bridge in the United States and the longest in the world that runs continuously over water. The causeway consists of two parallel bridges crossing Lake Pontchartrain in southern Louisiana, joining the north and south of the city of New Orleans. The longer of the two bridges is almost 24 miles in length (38.5km), and has held the Guinness World Record for the longest bridge in the world since 1969.

QUESTION

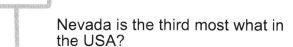

Nevada is the third most what in the USA?

A Seismically active state

B State with the lowest precipitation

C Most crime-ridden state

ANSWER

A   *Seismically active state*

Nevada is one of the most seismically active regions in the United States and is located in the Basin and Range province (a vast area that covers much of the inland Western United States and northwestern Mexico). California and Alaska are the only two other states which have had more large earthquakes over the last 150 years.

QUESTION

?

Cool, Nice, and Rough and Ready, are all towns in which state?

A New York

B California

C Florida

ANSWER

B *California*

Named after the Rough and Ready Mining Company, a group of gold prospectors from Wisconsin, so-named in honor of General Zachary "Old Rough and Ready" Taylor, who headed west and settled there in 1849.

QUESTION

?

What is the national animal of the United States?

A Bald eagle

B Grizzly bear

C Wolf

ANSWER

A   *Bald eagle*

The bald eagle was adopted as the national bird of the United States of America in 1782 and the American bison was adopted in May 2016 as the national mammal of the United States. Bald eagles are incredibly powerful, reputedly having been observed carrying a 14lbs (6.8kg) deer. In the wild they live on average for about 20 years, but have reached 38 years. In captivity, they can live to 50 years.

QUESTION

?

Oklahoma gave the world a first.
What was it?

A Pecan Pie

B Parking Meter

C Parachute

ANSWER

B *Parking Meter*

The world's first parking meter, known as Park-O-Meter No. 1, was installed on the southeast corner of what was then First Street and Robinson Avenue in Oklahoma City, Oklahoma, on July 16, 1935. Due to the abundance of cars being parked along the city roads by businessmen, shoppers no longer had anywhere to stop, which was increasingly becoming a problem for shopkeepers. Local newspaperman Magee sponsored a contest to design a timing device that would allocate set amounts of time for parking, which he and a partner went on to create. The rest is history.

QUESTION

?

Who wrote the Declaration of Independence?

A Thomas Jefferson

B George Washington

C Benjamin Franklin

A *Thomas Jefferson*

John Adams tasked Thomas Jefferson with writing the Declaration of Independence, which took him 17 days to write. No one knows who wrote the words "Original Declaration of Independence dated July 4th 1776" upside down on the reverse of the document but that simple inscription helps to ensure that the original copy remains safely protected by the government to this day.

QUESTION

?

Le Roy, New York, is home to which American favorite's gallery and museum?

A Betty Crocker

B Jell-O

C Hershey's

ANSWER

B *Jell-O*

It seems that a bowl of wobbly Jell-O has brain waves identical to those of adult men and women. No, seriously! Technicians at St. Jerome Hospital in Batavia, New York, tested a bowl of lime Jell-O with an EEG machine on March 17, 1993, which confirmed the earlier findings of neurologist, Dr. Adrian Upton. Why they both decided to test Jell-O for brain waves is anyone's guess.

144

QUESTION

?

The Phil Collins Collection in Texas is what?

A   A collection of the singer's platinum discs

B   A collection of the singer's Alamo artefacts

C   A collection of the singer's supercars

ANSWER

B *A collection of the singer's Alamo artefacts*

The fringed leather pouch that David Crockett carried his musket balls in the day he fell at the Alamo, probably started out its life in a Creek Indian village in Tennessee. Its trip to Texas with Crockett, in 1836, was just the start of a journey that would eventually land it in Switzerland, in the home of British pop legend Phil Collins. Crockett's pouch has now returned to the Alamo, and the rest of what is widely considered to be the biggest and best collection of Alamo artefacts ever assembled.

QUESTION

?

Approximately how long is the drive from the Grand Canyon's North Rim Visitor's Center to the South Rim Visitor's Center?

A 83 miles

B 215 miles

C 386 miles

ANSWER

B *215 miles*

The North and South Rims of the Grand Canyon are only 10 miles apart as the crow flies but around a 5 hour drive apart if following the rules of the road and there are no adverse conditions.

?

Which of the following President's faces is not carved on Mount Rushmore?

A   Abraham Lincoln

B   George Washington

C   John F. Kennedy

ANSWER

C *John F. Kennedy*

The four faces carved on Mount Rushmore are those of Abraham Lincoln, Thomas Jefferson, Theodore Roosevelt and George Washington. The carving of Mount Rushmore took 14 years, starting in 1927 and ending in 1941. A team of more than 400 men, many of whom had originally set out to mine for gold in the area, did the carving. Sculptor Gutzon Borglum, who designed, created and supervised the making of Mount Rushmore, chose each of the four presidents named, as he felt that they represented the first 150 years of American History.

QUESTION

?

What name did Walt Disney originally call his favorite mouse, until his wife suggested Mickey?

A Melvyn

B Mortimer

C Maurice

ANSWER

B *Mortimer*

Walt Disney originally named his mouse character Mortimer. However, his wife Lillian Disney wasn't as convinced by the name and suggested Mickey instead!

QUESTION

?

Hot Coffee, Money, and Whynot, are all communities in which state?

A Washington

B Arkansas

C Mississippi

ANSWER

C *Mississippi*

In 1870, L.J. Davis built a store and hung a coffee pot over the door that advertised 'the best hot coffee around.' The coffee was so popular that local politicians would visit Davis's store and buy coffee for constituents and passing travelers, leading to 'Hot Coffee' becoming the name of the community.

QUESTION

?

Whose star is the only one on the Hollywood Walk of Fame to be on a wall and not on the sidewalk?

A Frank Sinatra

B Muhammad Ali

C Judy Garland

ANSWER

B *Muhammad Ali*

Not wanting the name of Muhammad to be stepped on, Muhammad Ali requested that his Walk of Fame star be placed on a wall along the Hollywood Walk of Fame. Did you know that the original Hollywood sign was erected in 1921, at a cost of $21,000, as a billboard to sell land and property? Yes, it's true! It was a marketing sign for Hollywoodland Real Estate Development, owned by Los Angeles Times owner, Harry Chandler.

QUESTION

?

At which prestigious U.S. university can students become eligible to receive a pirate's license?

A   MIT, Cambridge, Massachusetts

B   Cornell, Ithaca, New York

C   Yale, New Haven, Connecticut

ANSWER

C *MIT, Cambridge, Massachusetts*

It's true! Well, sort of but don't tell Cap'n Jack! Any student at the Massachusetts Institute of Technology (MIT) who completes archery, fencing, sailing, and pistol (or rifle) classes is eligible to receive a pirate's license. Rum is not included!

QUESTION

?

Which state is home to Hershey's?

A Pennsylvania

B Massachusetts

C Illinois

ANSWER

A *Pennsylvania*

Apart from chocolate treats, The Hershey Chocolate Company also makes soap, which originally started as a way of making use of the millions of pounds of excess cocoa butter left over from production and is still sold in Hershey-owned stores.

QUESTION

?

What did Babe Ruth wear underneath his baseball cap?

A A toupee

B A cabbage leaf

C A frog

B   *A cabbage leaf*

Hall-of-Fame baseball player Babe Ruth needed to do what he could to keep cool in the intense heat of summer, especially as his uniform was made of wool. He came up with an idea that appears to have served him well, going by his immense success on the field. Babe Ruth would place pre-cooled cabbage leaves under his baseball cap and then swap them out for fresh ones every two innings. During his remarkable career he played for the Boston Red Sox (1914), the New York Yankees (1920) and the Atlanta Braves (1935).

QUESTION

? Who introduced his incandescent light bulb for the first time at the Southern Exposition in Kentucky, in 1883?

A Nikola Tesla

B Joseph Swan

C Thomas Edison

ANSWER

C *Thomas Edison*

The public was first introduced to the electric light bulb by inventor Thomas Edison at the Southern Exposition, held in Louisville in 1883. The exhibition was illuminated at night by the incredible spectacle of more than 4,500 of Edison's recently invented incandescent light bulbs.

QUESTION

?

What was the main source of fuel for American pioneers during the winter months?

A Wood

B Coal

C Oil

A *Wood*

Wood would be collected where possible during the day, as people traveled about. However, in areas such as the Great Plains, wood was a scarcity, so dried buffalo dung was collected and burned as an alternative fuel source.

QUESTION

?

When was the first car insurance policy written in America?

A 1872

B 1898

C 1904

ANSWER

B | *1898*

Travelers Insurance Company issued the first automobile insurance policy in the United States in 1898. The following year, the first fatal automobile accident happened in New York City when a pedestrian was sadly killed.

QUESTION

?

Which is the most Eastern city in the USA?

A Eastpoint

B Eastport

C Eastwick

ANSWER

B *Eastport*

Tourism is important to Eastport, which is a city and archipelago in Washington County, Maine, USA, with a population of under 1,500. It was originally developed as a center for canning sardines, but has diversified into farming Atlantic salmon, cultivating Nori seaweed, producing textiles, and shipping logs, and paper products from the port.

QUESTION

?

The four hotels at the corner of Las Vegas Blvd and Tropicana Ave have more rooms than which city?

A Key West

B Tucson

C San Francisco

ANSWER

C   *San Francisco*

San Francisco has more than 30,000 hotel rooms available across the city. Las Vegas has the most hotel rooms of any city worldwide with more than 150,000. It would take more than 400 years to spend a night in each of them. Orlando (Florida), Paris (France), and Barcelona (Spain) have the next highest availability of rooms.

QUESTION

?

Bourbon, Goodnight, and Conception Junction, are all places in which state?

A Missouri

B Ohio

C Tennessee

ANSWER

A   *Missouri*

The community of Goodnight, Missouri, according to the 2010 census only has a population of 18, and was named after a local mill owner J H Goodnight. Goodnight has a total area of 0.64 square miles (1.66 km^2), all of which is land.

QUESTION

?

The Louisiana Native Guards was the first American army to have what?

A   Female Officers

B   African American Officers

C   Gay Officers

ANSWER

B **African American Officers (Corps d'Afrique, September 27, 1862)**

The Louisiana Native Guards was a Union infantry regiment made up of African-American and mixed-race troops, with both white and black officers. It became the first African-American regiment to see battle in the Civil War when on May 27, 1863, they assaulted Confederate fortifications at Port Hudson, Louisiana.

QUESTION

?

Which was the 50th state to join the Union in 1959?

A Hawai'i

B Alaska

C Arizona

ANSWER

A   *Hawai'i*

Hawai'i joined the Union on August 21, 1959 and is located around 2,000 miles (3,200km) from the U.S. Mainland, and had been a U.S. Territory since 1898. It became a state after 93 percent of Hawai'ians voted positively about the proposition of being approved as a state. Apart from having incredible coastlines and a lush landscape, some of which were seen in the Jurassic Park movies, Hawai'i also has the largest amount of endangered species and the highest life expectancy in the country.

?

In November 1903, Mary Anderson was granted her first patent for what?

A Automatic windshield wipers

B Insulated travel flask

C Compact mirror

ANSWER

A   *Automatic windshield wipers*

At the time of Mary Anderson's invention, most cars went too slowly to even require a windshield. She invented the wipers after traveling on a trolley car in New York City, having visited from her home in Alabama, hoping to see the sights. Snow was falling and the driver kept having to stick his hand and sometimes his head out to clear the screen, which was her inspiration.

?

At one time it was illegal to serve what on Cherry Pie in Kansas?

A Custard

B Cream

C Ice cream

C *Ice cream*

No one knows why, or perhaps they just can't remember but it is illegal in Kansas to top a slice of cherry pie with a scoop of ice cream. The law is technically still active, but is no longer enforced.

?

Marlon Brando, Fred Astaire, and Warren Buffett were all born in Nebraska but which of the following also comes from there?

A Gatorade

B Band-Aid

C Kool-Aid

C *Kool-Aid*

Kool-Aid started out in the 1920s as 'Fruit Smack,' a fruit concentrate drink sold in six flavors by door-to-door salesmen. Due to bottle breakage and leakage issues, Edwin Perkins worked out how to remove the liquid from the concentrate and instead started to sell the flavored powder in envelopes instead, originally calling it Kool-Ade.

QUESTION

?

Three states have a law prohibiting people from carrying a certain food item in their back pockets. What is it?

A Dill pickle

B Fried fish

C Ice cream cone

ANSWER

C *Ice cream cone*

Odd as it may seem, there is logic to the law that prohibits the carrying of an ice cream cone in your back pocket, in Alabama, Georgia, and Kentucky. The reason given is that back when horses were more popular than cars, horse thieves would put ice cream in their back pockets to surreptitiously lure horses away without being charged with stealing.

QUESTION

?

Ducks still visit the lobby fountain at 11 a.m. and 5 p.m. each day at The Peabody Hotel, in which U.S. town?

A Manhattan

B Memphis

C Miami

ANSWER

B *Memphis*

The Peabody ducks are raised on a farm and only stay at the hotel for three months, after which time they go back home to the farm. Whilst at the hotel, they live in specially designed luxury accommodation on the roof of the hotel.

QUESTION

?

What American phenomenon was known as 'The Great White Way?

A Chicago's Miracle Mile

B Broadway, Manhattan, NYC

C Rodeo Drive, Beverly Hills, LA

ANSWER

B   *Broadway, New York City*

From 1910, a section of Broadway in Manhattan - specifically the area between 41st and 53rd Streets in the Theater District, close to Times Square - was illuminated by "more than a million lamps," as electricity and then the incandescent light bulb were introduced. Previously, theaters were originally lit by gas lamps so audiences were often at risk of fire and fumes but soon billboards, posters, and marquees that promoted plays and musicals were lit up like never before, gaining the nickname 'The Great White Way.'

QUESTION

?

Amelia Earhart, the first woman to fly solo across the Atlantic, was from which state?

A Kentucky

B Minnesota

C Kansas

C *Kansas*

Born in Atchison, Kansas, on July 24, 1897, Amelia Earhart took her first airplane ride with pilot Frank Hawks on December 28, 1920. Amelia was so taken with flying that she took her first lesson only six days later on January 3, 1921, and became the first woman to fly solo across the Atlantic in 1932. Little could she have imagined that far into the future, DEN (Denver International Airport) would be twice the size of Manhattan, with 53 square miles (137.8 square kilometers) of land, making it larger than the city boundaries of Boston, Miami, or San Francisco.

QUESTION

?

Pray, Nimrod, and Square Butte, are all towns in which state?

A Nebraska

B Oklahoma

C Montana

C *Montana*

It seems that there are actually two communities in Montana that are named Nimrod: one is located in Flathead County and the other in Granite County, which is now a Ghost Town. Nimrod, a biblical figure, was 'a mighty hunter' and the land in Montana was deemed a hunter's paradise, hence the name.

QUESTION

?

Just outside Atlanta, the picturesque community of Serenbe requires each of its 200-plus homes to include what?

A An indoor bathroom

B A fire-escape

C A porch

ANSWER

C A porch

Serenbe is a wellness community that is set among acres of preserved forests and meadows with miles of nature trails. The community is also home to a 25-acre organic farm that produces more than 300 varieties of fruits and vegetables, herbs, and flowers. Residents enjoy the freshest produce and world-class culinary experiences including edible landscaping, community herb gardens, and blueberry bushes along paths and sidewalks. That porch rule isn't sounding so odd now, is it?

?

In which year was Route 66 decommissioned?

A 1984

B 1985

C 1986

B   *1985*

President Eisenhower's support of the Interstate Systems led to the enactment of the 1956 Federal-Aid Highway Act, which established the program for funding and building it. The newer and faster interstate system bypassed Route 66, which led to businesses shutting and towns suffering from loss of tourism. Route 66 was officially decommissioned on June 27, 1985. The last town bisected by 'the Mother Road' is Williams, Arizona.

QUESTION

?

In which year was the first American diner established?

A 1872

B 1927

C 1935

A *1872*

The pre-cursor to diners was opened in Providence, Rhode Island in 1872 by Walter Scott, serving workers of the Providence Journal from a horse-drawn lunch wagon. In 1893, Charles Palmer received the first diner patent for his 'night lunch wagons' and 'fancy night cafes.'

QUESTION

?

In which direction must you drive from Detroit, Michigan, to get to Ontario, Canada?

A Due north

B Due south

C Northwest

ANSWER

B *Due south*

It's true! Parts of Michigan are further North than Canada, so by taking the Detroit Windsor Bridge, which connects the U.S. Interstates to Ontario's Highway 401, you can drive due south into Ontario, Canada.

QUESTION

Mardi Gras, in New Orleans, is celebrated at which time of year?

A Just before Christmas

B Just before Thanksgiving

C Just before Lent

ANSWER

C   *Just before Lent*

Mardi Gras is French for "Fat Tuesday.'"
"Carnival season" begins on January 6,
which is also known as the Twelfth Night,
and officially ends on Fat Tuesday, the day
people consume foods that they would
then 'give up' for Lent. At many of the
larger celebrations, you' are very likely to
hear the phrase "laissez les bon temps
rouler." It translates from French to "let the
good times roll" and is known as the official
greeting of Mardi Gras.

QUESTION

?

The Smokey Bear signs indicating the risk of forest fires across America, originated in which state?

A New Hampshire

B New Jersey

C New Mexico

ANSWER

C   *New Mexico*

Smokey Bear (not Smokey 'the' Bear), the living symbol used to educate Americans about forest fires, was a real life black bear cub. He was originally found by firefighters from Taos Pueblo, in New Mexico, during the 17,000 acres (69km^2) human-caused Capitan Gap Fire of 1950. Smokey lived out his days at the National Zoo in Washington, D.C. until his death in 1976.

QUESTION

?

How many National Parks are there currently in the United States?

A 38

B 52

C 63

ANSWER

C   *63*

There are currently 63 national parks in the United States, with the most famous examples being Yellowstone, Yosemite, and the Grand Canyon. On March 1, 1872, President Ulysses S. Grant signed the Yellowstone National Park Protection Act into law and the world's first national park was born. Some sources list Hot Springs in Arkansas as the first national park. It was set aside in 1832, forty years before Yellowstone was established, but was actually the nation's oldest national reservation. In 1921, an act of Congress established Hot Springs as a national park.

QUESTION

?

The Beach Boys, Willie Nelson, and Johnny Cash all performed at Mitchell's Corn Palace - the world's ONLY corn palace - which is in which state?

A South Carolina

B Kansas

C South Dakota

ANSWER

C *South Dakota*

The city's first Corn Palace was built in 1892. A permanent building was completed in 1921. Twelve colors or shades of corn are used to decorate the Corn Palace: red, brown, black, blue, white, orange, calico, yellow, and green. Themes change annually, with each ear of corn attached individually to create a specific scene.

QUESTION

?

The Statue of Liberty was gifted to the USA in 1885 by which nation?

A The Netherlands

B France

C Italy

B **France**

The Statue of Liberty was given as a gift to America by France, in honor of the alliance between the two countries during the American Revolution. It arrived in New York on June 17, 1885. The sculptor, Frederic Auguste Bartholdi, envisioned the Statue of Liberty as a magnificent Greek Goddess of the past, and also as the working men and women of today. In other news, I have no idea why there is an 8ft (2.5m), nearly naked statue of Arnold Schwarzenegger in Columbus, Ohio.

QUESTION

?

How tall is the world-famous 'Welcome to Fabulous Las Vegas' sign?

A 25ft (8m)

B 75ft (23m)

C 150ft (46m)

A   *25ft (8m)*

The sign is relatively small compared to many other neon signs in Las Vegas and is actually located outside the city limits, in Paradise. The iconic sign was designed in 1959 by Betty Willis, who was one of the first female commercial artists to ever work on neon signs. She sold the design without copyright for $4,000, which is why it is now featured on an abundance of tourist memorabilia.

QUESTION

?

The Liberty Bell, which was made by the Whitechapel Bell Foundry in London, England, which also made Big Ben, resides in which city?

A Philadelphia, Pennsylvania

B Washington D.C.

C Boston, Massachusetts

ANSWER

A   *Philadelphia, Pennsylvania*

In 1751, the Liberty Bell was made to mark the 50-year anniversary of William Penn's 1701 Charter of Privileges, which served as Pennsylvania's original Constitution. In 1777, the Bell was removed from Philadelphia and sent by guarded wagon train to Allentown, Pa., and was hidden in a church. It was feared that the British would melt the Bell and use it to make munitions. It was returned to Philadelphia the following year. When struck, the Liberty Bell gives off the note E-flat.

?

The Cabazon Dinosaurs were originally created to entice customers into what type of business?

A Water Park

B Amusement Park

C Restaurant

C   *Restaurant*

The dinosaurs were originally designed and created by Knott's Berry Farm sculptor and theme park artist Claude Bell, to bring more customers to his local restaurant, the Wheel Inn. He started with the 150ft-long (46m) Brontosaurus 'Dinny the Dinosaur,' and 65ft-tall (20m) Tyrannosaurus Rex 'Mr Rex,' which are visible from Southern California's Interstate 10 freeway to travelers passing by.

QUESTION

?

Two Egg, Mayo, and Lone Cabbage, are all towns in which state?

A Florida

B Louisiana

C Georgia

ANSWER

A   *Florida*

No one is sure how Two Egg got its name.
One story is it that during the Depression,
two boys used to bring two eggs from their
family farm to the local store to trade for
sugar. Locals started to call the place the
"two egg store," and it seems that the
name stuck.

QUESTION

?

Which state opted out of daylight savings time in 1945?

A Alaska

B Hawai'i

C Michigan

ANSWER

B *Hawai'i*

Not only do Hawai'ians not have to worry about changing their clocks backwards and forwards for daylight savings time, Hawai'i is the only state to have its own time zone - Hawai'i-Aleutian. The last DST was on September 30, 1945. Arizona also opted out of observing DST in 1968.

QUESTION

?

James White discovered the Carlsbad Caverns when mining for what?

A Gold

B Guano

C Coal

ANSWER

B *Guano*

Guano (bat feces) was mined from the hard to access Carlsbad Caverns in the early 20th Century, to be used as a fertilizer, as it is high in soil-enriching nitrates. It was also exploited until the late 19th century as a prime source of saltpeter, a key component of gunpowder. Guano is still mined in North America today, but only for a niche market.

QUESTION

?

Which of the states is known as 'The 'Show-Me State?'

A Missouri

B Oklahoma

C Washington

ANSWER

A *Missouri*

Rumor has it that in 1899, Willard Vandiver, a Missouri Congressman said, "frothy eloquence neither convinces nor satisfies me. I'm from Missouri, and you have got to show me." That's why today Missourians' license plates proclaim that they are 'the Show-Me State.'

QUESTION

?

Which of the 50 states has the longest official name?

A Massachusetts

B Pennsylvania

C Rhode Island

C   *Rhode Island*

The 'State of Rhode Island and Providence Plantations' is the longest official name of any state in the United States. It also happens to be the smallest state (by area), being only 37 miles wide and 48 miles long, with a shoreline on Narragansett Bay in the Atlantic Ocean, that runs for 400 miles. The state with the second longest name is the 'Commonwealth of Pennsylvania.'

QUESTION

?

Which of the states produces enough cotton to make 2 T-shirts for every American (that's around 600 million tees)?

A South Carolina

B Georgia

C Arizona

ANSWER

C *Arizona*

Despite the large quantities of cotton produced, Arizona isn't the largest cotton producer in the United States, Texas is. Texas has contributed around 40 percent of U.S. cotton production in recent years. Overall, America is the third largest cotton producer after India, and China, in the world.

QUESTION

?

Where in America can tourists mine their own diamonds from their natural source?

A Arkansas

B Texas

C Alabama

ANSWER

A   *Arkansas*

The 37-acre field, in Murfreesboro, Arkansas, that makes up the Arkansas' Crater of Diamonds State Park, is one of the only places in the world where the public can search for real diamonds in their original volcanic source. The site is maintained by the park and visitors are allowed to keep any diamonds they discover. The park also offers a complimentary identification and registration of the gems.

QUESTION

?

Americans drive on the right hand side of the road but what percentage of the world drives on the left-hand side of the road?

A 15%

B 35%

C 50%

B   *35%*

England is probably the first country that comes to mind, but it is not the only country that drives on the left. The populations of Japan, Malta, Cyprus, Indonesia, Ireland, and most of the old English empire countries including India, Australia, New Zealand, and a number of African countries do, too.

QUESTION

?

Where is the Ben & Jerry's Flavor Graveyard located?

A Portland, Maine

B Waterbury, Vermont

C Lancaster, Pennsylvania

B   *Waterbury, Vermont*

The Flavor Graveyard was erected on a hill overlooking the Ben & Jerry's factory in 1997, complete with granite headstones, and witty epitaphs for each flavor's demise. It originally held just four flavors, which only existed in the United States: Dastardly Mash, Economic Crunch, Ethan Almond and Tuskegee Chunk, but has since grown to include over 35 flavors.

QUESTION

?

Jot 'Em Down Store, Hopeulikit and Experiment, are all places in which state?

A Pennsylvania

B Texas

C Georgia

ANSWER

C   *Georgia*

The most widely accepted tale about how Hopeulikit got its name, is that this name was selected during a contest to name its main dance hall. Someone had written 'Hopeulikit' at the bottom of one of the suggestion forms. The judges did like it, and decided that that would be the name of the town.

QUESTION

?

Which of the following things will you never see in Hawai'i because it is illegal there?

A   Red cars

B   Billboards

C   Silly string

B *Billboards*

The beautiful scenery in Hawai'i will never be interrupted by billboards because they are illegal. Three other scenically beautiful states also currently ban billboards: Alaska, Maine, and Vermont, making sure that the incredible landscapes in these picturesque states are never marred by advertisements.

QUESTION

? Elvis Presley's home 'Graceland' was named after the original landowner who was?

A Grace Foot

B Grace Fett

C Grace Toof

ANSWER

C   *Grace Toof*

Graceland was originally a 500-acre farm that belonged to the Toof family, from before the Civil War. The farm was developed by S.C. Toof's granddaughter, Ruth Brown Moore, and her husband, Dr. Thomas Moore in 1939, when they built the soon to be world-famous mansion. Ruth Brown Moore named the property after her aunt Grace Toof, who had inherited the land from her father, S.C. Toof. When Grace died, her sister inherited it, who bequeathed it to her daughter, Ruth. Elvis Presley bought the property on March 25, 1957.

QUESTION

?

Agawam, Massachusetts is known for being the first place to have what?

A A sewage system

B Traffic lights

C ZIP codes

ANSWER

C   *ZIP codes*

The first ZIP code in the United States was issued to Agawam, Massachusetts, and is 01001. It is the lowest ZIP code in the contiguous United States. ZIP stands for Zone Improvement Plan and was introduced July 1, 1963, to improve the speed of mail delivery.

QUESTION

?

Chocolate High, Talcum Passage, and The Rookery in New Mexico are what?

A Nightclubs

B Caves

C Districts

ANSWER

B   *Caves*

Carlsbad Caverns National Park is designated a World Heritage Site, and a United States National Park. Currently, 120 caves have been discovered, including Chocolate High, Talcum Passage and The Rookery, with the possibility of more as exploration continues. At around 150 miles, Lecheguilla is the eighth longest cave in the world and the largest in the park.

QUESTION

?

Where was the first phone directory published in the United States?

A Manhattan, New York

B New Haven, Connecticut

C Boston, Massachusetts

B   *New Haven, Connecticut*

The first phone directory, containing only 50 names, was published in New Haven, in February, 1878. It was created by Civil War veteran, George Coy, who had been present at a demonstration of the telephone by its inventor, Alexander Graham Bell, in April, 1877. On January 28, 1878, Coy was the first person to establish the world's first public telephone exchange.

QUESTION

?

Which rock star was banned from visiting The Alamo for 10 years, for urinating on the cenotaph?

A Ozzy Osbourne

B Axl Rose

C Jerry Lee Lewis

A   *Ozzy Osbourne*

On Feb. 19, 1982, Ozzy Osbourne urinated within the Alamo Plaza. He was arrested, charged with public intoxication, and spent part of the afternoon in jail. Later that day, he was freed on a $40 bond. Osbourne was also banned from playing San Antonio again until 1992, when he made a public apology to the city and donated $10,000 to the Daughters of the Republic of Texas, the organization that maintains the Alamo grounds.

QUESTION

?

What is Area 51?

A A famous nightclub in New York City

B A centimeter-wavelength radio astronomy observatory

C A United States Air Force military installation in Nevada

ANSWER

C **A U.S. Air Force military installation in Nevada**

Conspiracy theorists and paranormal enthusiasts believe Area 51 to be the location where the United States government stores and hides alien bodies and UFOs, including the flying saucer that allegedly crashed at Roswell, New Mexico, in 1947. The official name for Area 51 is the Nevada Test and Training Range, which is a unit of the Nellis Air Force Base. The name 'Area 51,' according to the CIA, comes from its map designation.

QUESTION

?

The town of Salem, of the infamous witch trials, is in which state?

A Oregon

B Massachusetts

C New Jersey

ANSWER

B *Massachusetts*

The Salem Witch Trials took place in
Salem Village, a small Puritan community
in the Massachusetts Bay Colony, from
February, 1692 until May, 1693. They were
a succession of investigations and
hearings that explored accusations of
witchcraft. Around 200 people were
accused of witchcraft, 19 of whom were
executed and 5 of whom were men.

QUESTION

?

Beer Bottle Crossing, Ozone, and Slickpoo, are all towns in which state?

A Idaho

B Indiana

C Illinois

ANSWER

A   *Idaho*

Slickpoo was named after Josiah Slickpoo who helped Idaho's infamous Father Cataldo expand his Jesuit mission across southern Idaho, by providing a site for his church, and Ozone was originally a rural stage coach stop, named after the stage coach company, Ozone. No one knows how Beer Bottle Crossing got its name.

QUESTION

?

If your name is in the Las Vegas 'Black Book,' you are what?

A   Banned from every casino in town

B   A super high roller having spent at least $1 million gambling in the city

C   A winner of at least $1 million from a competitive poker game

ANSWER

A *Banned from every casino in town*

Apparently, it's harder to get into the Las Vegas 'Black Book' than to win an Oscar. Formally known as the Nevada Gaming Control Board (GCB) Excluded Person List. Created in 1973 with two originating members, Hawai'ian crime syndicate racketeers Alvin George Kaohu and Wilford Kalaauala Pulawa, it has had only 32 names added since, including Archie Karas.

?

Indian River, Michigan, is home to the largest what in the world?

A Shoe

B Teapot

C Crucifix

ANSWER

C *Crucifix*

The Cross in the Woods was originally erected in 1954, carved from a Redwood tree, cut from the mountains in Oregon. The Crucifix is 55ft (17m) high, 22ft (7m) wide, weighs 7 tons, is 28ft (8.5m) from top to toe, and the outstretched arms span 21ft (6m). It was completed in 1959, when renowned Michigan sculptor, Marshall M. Fredericks, created the bronze image of Jesus. The largest United States collection of religious dolls is also housed onsite.

QUESTION

?

Michael Carmichael created the world's largest what?

A   Painted baseball

B   Pizza

C   Bar of soap

ANSWER

A *Painted baseball*

After dropping a baseball in paint more than 50 years ago, in Alexandria, Iowa, Michael Carmichael has since created the world's largest painted ball. He has added a new coat of paint or two every year since then, so that the ball now weighs a colossal 4,000lbs and has a 14ft (4m) circumference.

?

What was the largest currency note ever used in America?

A $100

B $1,000

C $10,000

C $10,000

They really did exist, but you might have never seen a $10,000 bill, for a number of reasons, but mainly because the government stopped producing them in 1969. The first coin ever produced in the United States was the 'Fugio' cent (Latin for 'I fly'), possibly called this to remind everyone that money and time flies. Most interestingly, rather than having the words, 'In God We Trust' on it, which appeared after the Civil War, this penny said, 'Mind Your Business.'

QUESTION

? There's a house in Rockport, Massachusetts, made entirely of what?

A Glass bottles

B Newspaper

C Plastic cartons

ANSWER

B *Newspaper*

In 1922, a mechanical engineer, Elis F. Stenman, who incidentally designed the machines that make paper clips, began building his Rockport summer home out of paper, including some beautiful pieces of furniture too. Meanwhile, in Houston, Texas, it took John Milkovisch 18 years to build a 'house' out of over 50,000 beer cans, with a lawn that has concrete blocks inlaid with colorful glass, a holey fence filled with marbles, and porch curtains made of ring tabs.

?

Which state offers the highest recycling refund in the country, as seen on Seinfeld?

A Maine

B Michigan

C Maryland

ANSWER

C *Michigan*

Michigan (89%), and Oregon (86%), have the highest return rates of eligible beverage containers returned by consumers for recycling, of the 10 U.S. bottle bill states. This is largely attributed to the generous 10 cent deposit, which appears to offer a compelling incentive to return used beverage containers. The states with a lower return rate only offer 5 cents per item, except for liquor bottles for which they offer 15 cents.

QUESTION

?

In which state is Pikes Peak Mountain to be found?

A Oregon

B Colorado

C Montana

ANSWER

B *Colorado*

Pikes Peak is a designated National Historic Landmark, and is one of Colorado's 53 'fourteeners;' mountains that are more than 14,000ft (4,267m) above sea level. It was named after American explorer Zebulon Pike, who called the mountain "Highest Peak," in 1806. It was finally named "Pikes Peak" by the United States Board on Geographic Names, in 1890. Not even close to 14,000ft above sea level is Oregon landmark, Haystack Rock, a 235ft tall (72m) sea stack, in Cannon Beach. It is home to numerous sea birds, and made a memorable appearance in 'The Goonies' movie.

QUESTION

?

Michigan has 124 of what?

A Cathedrals

B Prisons

C Lighthouses

ANSWER

C *Lighthouses*

The first lighthouse was built in 1829, by Lucius Lyon, in what would later become the state of Michigan. Named for a nearby military outpost the Fort Gratiot Light was constructed on Lake Huron and still stands to this day.

QUESTION

?

The Pink Rattlesnake is a species only found where?

A Grand Canyon

B Death Valley

C Mojave Desert

ANSWER

A   *Grand Canyon*

There are several types of snake that can be found at the Grand Canyon, six of which are rattlesnakes. The three most common are the Mojave 'Green', Great Basin, and Grand Canyon Pink Rattlesnakes, with the 'Pink' only being found here, mainly at the North Rim. It grows from 16" to 54" in length. The Mojave 'Green' Rattlesnake is the most venomous in all of North America.

QUESTION

?

If the giant milk bottle displayed at the Children's Museum in Boston, were real, how much milk could it hold?

A 5,000 gallons

B 25,000 gallons

C 50,000 gallons

ANSWER

C   *50,000 gallons*

The milk bottle - large enough to hold 58,620 gallons if it were real - first appeared in 1934, as a roadside stand for ice cream maker Arthur Gagner, who used it to entice drivers from Route 44 in Taunton. Abandoned in 1967, it was later repaired and donated to the Museum in 1977, and now houses a little restaurant, too.

?

What item with an ironic slogan do inmates in New Hampshire make?

A T-shirts

B License plates

C Baseball caps

ANSWER

B *License plates*

It's true! Prison inmates in New Hampshire's state prison in Concord, really do stamp license plates with the state motto, "Live Free or Die."

QUESTION

?

Dry Prong, Cut Off, and Waterproof, are all towns in which state?

A Louisiana

B Georgia

C Alabama

A *Louisiana*

The names of all three towns have connections to water. Dry Prong was named by a sawmill owner whose water wheel was in a creek that dried out every summer. A canal that was meant to connect Bayou Lafourche via Lake Salvador with New Orleans, did not, so it was Cut Off. Finally, Waterproof, because despite flooding being a big problem in Louisiana, this area is rarely affected.

QUESTION

?

Which is the only state that has a longer shoreline than Michigan?

A Alaska

B California

C Florida

ANSWER

A *Alaska*

Alaska and it's 2,670 named islands has
66,000 miles of Arctic and sub-Arctic
shorelines and coastal ecosystems that
include glacial fjords, 52 active volcanoes,
a delta that is 12 times larger than the
Mississippi Delta, inlets, bays, parks, and
refuges.

QUESTION

?

The song, "Happy Birthday To You," was written by two sisters in 1893, who were from where?

A Louisville, Kentucky

B Telluride, Colorado

C Bar Harbor, Maine

ANSWER

A   *Louisville, Kentucky*

The story is that sisters, Patty and Mildred Hill, published a song in 1893, called 'Good Morning To All,' for their kindergarten students to sing. One day, to celebrate a child's birthday, the class changed to words to 'Happy Birthday to You' and the rest is history.

QUESTION

?

Colon, Michigan, is known for being what?

A The pinball capital of the world

B The crazy golf capital of the world

C The magic capital of the world

ANSWER

C — *The magic capital of the world*

Harry Blackstone, one of the most famous magicians in America in the mid-1920s, chose Colon as the summer residence for his massive traveling illusion show. Blackstone invited Australian magician Percy Abbott to visit him, who then married a local woman. Both magicians formed the Blackstone Magic Company, selling magician's supplies. After falling out, Abbott established Abbott's Magic Company in Colon, becoming the largest manufacturer and retailer of magic equipment in the world.

QUESTION

?

What well-known product is manufactured in Cynthiana, Kentucky?

A Pepsi Cola

B Post It Notes

C Pillsbury Dough

ANSWER

B *Post It Notes*

Originally named 'Press n' Peel,' Post It Notes were created by accident, when Spencer Silver, a 3M scientist, was trying to create a super strong adhesive and instead created a reusable one by chance. The bright yellow notes also happened by chance - it was the colour of the scrap paper used when testing out the glue and is still the most popular choice of all.

QUESTION

?

Which city is known as the car capital of the world?

A Denver, Colorado

B Dayton, Ohio

C Detroit, Michigan

ANSWER

C *Detroit, Michigan*

Detroit, once the center of the automotive industry, known as Motown (Motor Town), developed by chance, as Henry Ford and Ransom Olds, pioneers of the industry, just happened to live nearby, in Greenfield Township and Lansing, respectively.

?

What unusual problem has Centralia, Pennsylvania, suffered from since 1960?

A Constant rainfall

B Smells of sulphur

C Is on fire

ANSWER

C   *Is on fire*

Centralia, was once a bustling mining town but a fire, which started in an underground coal seam in May, 1962, has been burning ever since, leaving it almost no more than a ghost town, with only a handful of residents (as of 2020).

QUESTION

?

In which state is the Cape Canaveral Air Force Station to be found?

A Washington D.C.

B Nevada

C Florida

ANSWER

C   *Florida*

Renamed in December 2020, to the Cape Canaveral Space Force Station, the area has been used to test missiles since 1949. Launches can be made out over the Atlantic Ocean, and as it is closer to the equator than most other parts of the United States, rockets get a boost from the Earth's rotation.

QUESTION

?

Which letter of the alphabet is not used in any of the 50 state names?

A   J

B   Z

C   Q

ANSWER

C   Q

No state names use the letter 'Q.' J is used in New Jersey and Z is used in Arizona.

QUESTION

?

Approximately how many couples get married in Las Vegas each month?

A 5,000

B 10,000

C 15,000

ANSWER

B   *10,000*

The most popular days of the year to get married in Las Vegas are St Valentine's Day and New Year's Eve but every day in Sin City is wedding day with around 300 ceremonies being performed each day.

QUESTION

?

Mianus is a town that can be found in which state?

A Connecticut

B Arizona

C Maryland

A   *Connecticut*

Mianus is in Greenwich, Connecticut, and was named after chief Sachem Myn Myano, whose name meant 'he who gathers together.' The Veterans Administration and the town created a village of 40 starter homes after World War II, to be rented by returning servicemen and their families…and that's all we are going to say about the name, unlike 'Jackass,' the TV show!

QUESTION

?

How many federally recognised Native American tribes are there in the United States?

A 127

B 312

C 574

ANSWER

C   *574*

Of these 574 federally recognized tribes, 229 are in Alaska, with California having the second-highest number of tribes with 109, as well as having the largest Native American population of any state.

QUESTION

?

How much can an elk's antlers grow each day?

A 1 mm

B 1 cm

C 1 inch

ANSWER

C   *1 inch*

Only male elk have antlers, which they shed and grow anew every year. Their new antlers are covered in fuzzy skin called velvet, which peels away by late summer, when the antlers have turned to solid bone, and weigh up to 40lbs (18kg).

QUESTION

?

How many time zones are there in N. America?

A 3

B 4

C 6

ANSWER

C   6

United States time zones were created after railroads lobbied the government to create times zones in order to have an accurate timetable. The six United States time zones are Hawai'i-Aleutian time (HST), Alaska time (AKST), Pacific time (PST), Mountain time (MST), Central time (CST), and Eastern time (EST).

Printed in Great Britain
by Amazon